Think → Write → Share

TAGAKI

Advanced 3

JN089242

SDGs : Problems & Solutions

Learn about sustainable development goals (SDGs)
Research a topic and write about a problem and a solution

TAGAKI Advanced 3 is based on the 17 sustainable development goals (SDGs) that were set by the UN in 2015. These goals will only be achieved if all countries, regardless of economic status, including their government bodies, private enterprises, organizations, groups and individuals, take part. To discuss issues that affect the whole world, it is best to study them using a common language.

The topics are simplified to one goal for each unit for ease of understanding and to enable users to personally Acknowledge --> Consider --> Act. The units are designed to first explain one aspect of each goal, and then introduce a solution for it. Users are asked to find a similar or related topic in their own country and suggest a way to resolve it. There are many problems in the world and many ways to resolve them. We hope this workbook will be a starting point for us to tackle some of these issues.

TAGAKI Advanced 3

SDGs: Problems and Solutions

Contents

Goals

How to use

TAGAKI Advanced 3 SDGs: Problems and Solutions

1

Learn about one of the SDGs by reading the comic and the fact box. Listen to the audio.

Please note that the audio recording of this book contains pronunciations of some words as commonly spoken by users of American English.

2

Check your understanding by answering five questions.
(Sample answers are on page 76-79)

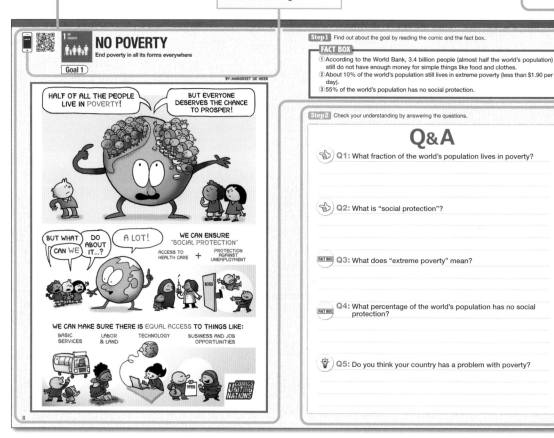

How to write your own version

Title	Use the research topic you chose as a title.
Introduction	Write at least one sentence to introduce your opinion. If you can't think of an original introduction, you can copy the one in the sample.
Problem	Use your research to write about the problem in your country.
Solution	Use your research to write about what people are trying to do to solve this problem in your country.
Reaction	Write what you think about the problem and/or solution.
Actions	Write what actions you can take in your own life to help reach the goal.

Useful Expressions
Use some of the useful expressions, if you like.

3

Read the sample sentences to find out what one country is doing to reach the goal.
Listen to the audio.

4

Use one of the topics from the possible research topics, or think of something else.
Search about your own country.

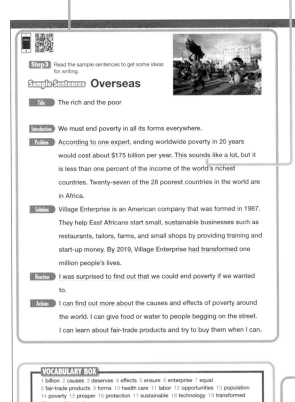

Step3 Read the sample sentences to get some ideas for writing.

Sample Sentences Overseas

Title The rich and the poor

Introduction We must end poverty in all its forms everywhere.

Problem According to one expert, ending worldwide poverty in 20 years would cost about $175 billion per year. This sounds like a lot, but it is less than one percent of the income of the world's richest countries. Twenty-seven of the 28 poorest countries in the world are in Africa.

Solution Village Enterprise is an American company that was formed in 1987. They help East Africans start small, sustainable businesses such as restaurants, tailors, farms, and small shops by providing training and start-up money. By 2019, Village Enterprise had transformed one million people's lives.

Reaction I was surprised to find out that we could end poverty if we wanted to.

Actions I can find out more about the causes and effects of poverty around the world. I can give food or water to people begging on the street. I can learn about fair-trade products and try to buy them when I can.

VOCABULARY BOX
1 billion 2 causes 3 deserves 4 effects 5 ensure 6 enterprise 7 equal
8 fair-trade products 9 forms 10 health care 11 labor 12 opportunities 13 population
14 poverty 15 prosper 16 protection 17 sustainable 18 technology 19 transformed
20 unemployment

Step4 Research something to do with the topic. Write around 150 words. Use some of the useful expressions, if you like.

Possible Research Topics
Hints
- The rich and the poor
- Fair-trade products
- Low wages
- Homeless people

In my country

Title

Introduction

Problem

Solution

Reaction

Actions

Reference

Step5 After writing, share your ideas with your friends.

This box gives you vocabulary that helps you to understand the goal.
Try to use some of these when you write.

Listen to the sample sentences the way they are spoken with contractions.

5

Write a reference to the source of your data.

6

Present what you wrote by reading it out loud, or even better, memorize it, then present it.

A TO DO LIST FOR THE PLANET

BY: MARGREET DE HEER

THE GLOBAL GOALS
For Sustainable Development

WHAT YOU CAN DO!

BY: MARGREET DE HEER

BUT WHAT CAN WE DO?

WE ARE NOT IN GOVERNMENT OR ANYTHING...

THE MOST IMPORTANT THING IS THAT WE ALL GET ON THE SAME PAGE! HERE'S WHAT YOU CAN DO:

1. THINK ABOUT IT

2. TALK ABOUT IT

3. DREAM ABOUT IT

4. WRITE ABOUT IT

5. MAKE ART ABOUT IT

6. ACT ON IT

COMICS UNITING NATIONS

BY: MARGREET DE HEER

FACT BOX

① According to the World Bank, 3.4 billion people (almost half the world's population) still do not have enough money for simple things like food and clothes.

② About 10% of the world's population still lives in extreme poverty (less than $1.90 per day).

③ 55% of the world's population has no social protection.

Step2 Check your understanding by answering the questions.

Q&A

 **Q1:** What fraction of the world's population lives in poverty?

 **Q2:** What is "social protection"?

FACT BOX **Q3:** What does "extreme poverty" mean?

FACT BOX **Q4:** What percentage of the world's population has no social protection?

Q5: Do you think your country has a problem with poverty?

Step3 Read the sample sentences to get some ideas for writing.

Sample Sentences **Overseas**

Title The rich and the poor

Introduction We must end poverty in all its forms everywhere.

Problem According to one expert, ending worldwide poverty in 20 years would cost about $175 billion per year. This sounds like a lot, but it is less than one percent of the income of the world's richest countries. Twenty-seven of the 28 poorest countries in the world are in Africa.

Solution Village Enterprise is an American company that was formed in 1987. They help East Africans start small, sustainable businesses such as restaurants, tailors, farms, and small shops by providing training and start-up money. By 2019, Village Enterprise had transformed one million people's lives.

Reaction I was surprised to find out that we could end poverty if we wanted to.

Actions I can find out more about the causes and effects of poverty around the world. I can give food or water to people begging on the street. I can learn about fair-trade products and try to buy them when I can.

VOCABULARY BOX

1 billion 2 causes 3 deserves 4 effects 5 ensure 6 enterprise 7 equal
8 fair-trade products 9 forms 10 health care 11 labor 12 opportunities 13 population
14 poverty 15 prosper 16 protection 17 sustainable 18 technology 19 transformed
20 unemployment

Step 4 Research something to do with the topic. Write around 150 words. Use some of the useful expressions, if you like.

Hints

Possible Research Topics

☐ The rich and the poor
☐ Fair-trade products
☐ Low wages
☐ Homeless people

In my country

Title

Introduction

Problem

Solution

Reaction

Actions

Reference

Step 5 After writing, share your ideas with your friends.

2 ZERO HUNGER

ZERO HUNGER

End hunger, achieve food security and improved nutrition and promote sustainable agriculture

Goal 2

BY: MARGREET DE HEER

FACT BOX

① Hunger is one of the leading causes of death in the world.
② 820 million people worldwide do not have enough food.
③ In 2019, 191 million children under the age of 5 had problems from serious malnutrition.

Step 2 Check your understanding by answering the questions.

Q&A

 Q1: What does eating only one sort of food cause?

 Q2: How can we end malnutrition?

 Q3: What is one of the leading causes of death in the world?

 Q4: How many people do not have enough food?

 Q5: Do you think your country has a problem with too much food or too little food?

Step3 Read the sample sentences to get some ideas for writing.

  **Overseas**

| Title | Community kitchens |

| Introduction | We need to end hunger, achieve food security and improved nutrition, and promote sustainable agriculture. |

| Problem | People need food before they can achieve good levels of health and wealth. A lack of food has been a problem in Malawi for decades. Research shows that 37 percent of Malawian children under the age of five do not grow properly because of serious malnutrition. |

| Solution | The Sikh religion has a tradition called Langar. This is a community kitchen which provides free meals. A Sikh organization from the UK called "Zero Hunger with Langar" serves over 100,000 meals a month to hungry and malnourished people in Malawi. |

| Reaction | I thought it was wonderful that the Sikh religion has a tradition of helping feed people. |

| Actions | I will donate some money on my birthday on the "Zero Hunger with Langar" website. I want to learn more about the dangers of malnutrition from too little food or too much of the same kind of food. |

VOCABULARY BOX

1 achieve 2 agriculture 3 community kitchens 4 crops 5 education 6 flooding 7 hunger
8 improved 9 indigenous 10 malnutrition 11 manage 12 manure 13 natural disasters
14 nutrition 15 obesity 16 prevent 17 promote 18 protect 19 provides 20 religion
21 security 22 variety

Step4 Research something to do with the topic. Write around 150 words. Use some of the useful expressions, if you like.

Possible Research Topics

Hints
- ☐ Community kitchens
- ☐ Obesity and malnutrition
- ☐ Food waste
- ☐ Food banks

In my country

Title

Introduction

Problem

Solution

Reaction

Actions

 **Reference**

Step5 After writing, share your ideas with your friends.

GOOD HEALTH AND WELL-BEING

3 GOOD HEALTH AND WELL-BEING

Goal 3

Ensure healthy lives and promote well-being for all at all ages

BY: MARGREET DE HEER

GOOD HEALTH AND WELL-BEING...?

WHAT DOES THAT REALLY MEAN...?

IT MEANS THINGS LIKE THIS:

1. A SAFE AND HEALTHY BIRTH FOR MOTHER AND CHILD

CHILD BIRTH CAN BE PRETTY DANGEROUS! WITH PROFESSIONAL SUPPORT THE RISK OF DEATH OR COMPLICATIONS IS MINIMIZED.

2. LIVING THROUGH EARLY CHILDHOOD

CHILDREN UNDER THE AGE OF FIVE ARE ESPECIALLY VULNERABLE. THEIR HEALTH CAN BE STRENGTHENED BY VACCINATIONS AND PROPER FOOD.

3. PROTECTION FROM PREVENTABLE DISEASES

EPIDEMICS CAN BE PREVENTED AND MANAGED. PEOPLE WHO CONTRACT A CONTAGIOUS DISEASE MUST GET QUALITY TREATMENT.

4. FREEDOM FROM ADDICTION

EDUCATE PEOPLE ABOUT ADDICTION AND PROVIDE TREATMENT FOR AFFECTED PEOPLE.

5. KNOWING YOUR BODY AND RIGHTS

IMPROVE INFORMATION ABOUT – AND ACCESS TO – SERVICES RELATED TO SEXUAL AND REPRODUCTIVE HEALTH.

6. ACCESS TO HEALTH CARE

PROVIDE ACCESS TO ESSENTIAL HEALTHCARE SERVICES, MEDICINES AND VACCINATION FOR ALL.

COMICS UNITING NATIONS

16

FACT BOX

① At least half the world's population still do not have the health services they need.
② Only half of women in developing regions receive the amount of health care they need.
③ Air pollution kills 7 million people each year, making it one of the world's largest environmental health risks.

Step 2 Check your understanding by answering the questions.

Q&A

 Q1: What does good health and well-being mean?

 Q2: What kind of health care can we provide for all?

FACT BOX **Q3:** What percentage of women in developing regions receive the health care they need?

FACT BOX **Q4:** What is one of the world's largest environmental health risks?

Q5: What diseases have you been vaccinated against?

Step3 Read the sample sentences to get some ideas for writing.

Sample Sentences **Overseas**

Title Technology addiction

Introduction We must ensure healthy lives and promote well-being for all at all ages.

Problem The world is healthier than ever before. However, modern lifestyles can lead to new health problems, such as technology addiction. In 2002, a 24-year-old Korean man died after playing online video games for 86 hours straight at a cyber cafe.

Solution In 2011, Korea passed the "Shutdown Law" which made it illegal for children under 16 to play online games between midnight and six a.m. However, one recent report found that teens only got 90 seconds more sleep after the law was brought in. The reason could be that many people now own a smartphone and are on it from the time they wake up to the moment they go to sleep.

Reaction I could not believe that someone actually died from playing games for too long.

Actions I will limit the time I spend on video games. I will regularly take time off my phone and try to have meals without it. I will stop using it an hour before bedtime, so I can sleep properly.

VOCABULARY BOX

1 addiction 2 affected 3 air pollution 4 birth 5 complications 6 contagious 7 contract
8 developing regions 9 environmental 10 epidemics 11 essential 12 illegal 13 medicines
14 minimized 15 preventable 16 proper 17 quality 18 reproductive 19 rights
20 strengthened 21 treatment 22 vaccinations 23 vulnerable 24 well-being

Step4 Research something to do with the topic. Write around 150 words. Use some of the useful expressions, if you like.

Possible Research Topics

Hints
- ☐ Technology addiction
- ☐ Other addictions (alcohol, gambling, drugs)
- ☐ Air pollution
- ☐ Contagious diseases

In my country

Title

Introduction

Problem

Solution

Reaction

Actions

Reference

Step5 After writing, share your ideas with your friends.

BY: MARGREET DE HEER

FACT BOX

① Education helps many other Sustainable Development Goals (SDGs). For example, it helps people to escape poverty.
② 750 million adults still cannot read and write.
③ 57 million elementary age children around the world remain out of school. Around 50% of them live in war zones.

Step 2 Check your understanding by answering the questions.

Q&A

 Q1: When is the best time to start education?

 Q2: What kind of environment is best?

 Q3: How many adults worldwide cannot read and write?

 Q4: How many children around the world are not in school?

 Q5: Do you think you are getting a quality education? Why?

Step3 Read the sample sentences to get some ideas for writing.

Sample Sentences **Overseas**

Title Lifelong learning

Introduction We must ensure inclusive and equitable quality education and promote lifelong learning opportunities for all.

Problem Education transforms lives, but not everyone wants to or is able to send their children to school. Margarita Pelico was born in a village in Guatemala, where most people became weavers or farmers. She wanted to go to school, but her parents did not think it was important, so they did not send her to elementary school.

Solution When Margarita was 13, she discovered a free correspondence program that the Guatemalan government provided with support from UNESCO. She completed her education and now owns two weaving and textile factories. She also trains other women so they can support themselves.

Reaction I did not realize that some children around the world do not go to school.

Actions I will work hard at school to make the most of my educational opportunities. I can start an SDGs Club at school to educate other students. I can discuss the SDGs with my friends and think more deeply about them.

VOCABULARY BOX

1 available 2 correspondence 3 discrimination 4 environment 5 equally 6 equitable
7 funding 8 inclusive 9 lifelong 10 motivated 11 positive 12 rights-respecting
13 scholarships 14 textile 15 war zones 16 weavers 17 well-trained

Step4 Research something to do with the topic. Write around 150 words. Use some of the useful expressions, if you like.

Hints

Possible Research Topics

- ☐ Lifelong learning
- ☐ Well-trained and motivated teachers
- ☐ Bullying/Discrimination in education
- ☐ Scholarships and financial support

In my country

Title

Introduction

Problem

Solution

Reaction

Actions

Reference

Step5 After writing, share your ideas with your friends.

5 GENDER EQUALITY

GENDER EQUALITY

Achieve gender equality and empower all women and girls

Goal 5

BY: MARGREET DE HEER

WOMEN AND GIRLS WORLDWIDE OFTEN LIVE DISADVANTAGED LIVES! HERE'S WHAT WE CAN DO ABOUT IT!

1. END ALL VIOLENCE AGAINST WOMEN AND GIRLS

INCLUDING TRAFFICKING, SEXUAL EXPLOITATION, FORCED MARRIAGE AND FEMALE GENITAL MUTILATION

2. RECOGNIZE AND VALUE WOMEN'S WORK AT HOME

3. ENCOURAGE WOMEN AND GIRLS

TO PARTICIPATE IN ALL POLITICAL, ECONOMIC AND PUBLIC SPHERES

4. EQUAL RIGHTS UNDER THE LAW

FACT BOX

① Women represent 39% of the workforce but only 27% of managerial positions.
② Globally, almost 750 million women and girls were married before the age of 18.
③ 1 in 5 women and girls has experienced physical and/or sexual violence by a partner within the last 12 months.

Step 2 Check your understanding by answering the questions.

Q&A

Q1: What examples of violence against women and girls are given?

Q2: What can we encourage women and girls to do?

FACT BOX **Q3:** How many women and girls were married before the age of 18?

FACT BOX **Q4:** What proportion of women and girls have experienced violence by a partner?

Q5: Do you think the genders are equal in your country?

Step3 Read the sample sentences to get some ideas for writing.

Sample Sentences Overseas

Title Gender equality

Introduction We must achieve gender equality and empower all women and girls.

Problem Women and girls are half of the world's population and half of its potential. Nevertheless, gender inequality is still common and slows social progress. In India, male children are more highly valued than females, and there are high levels of violence against women. One 2018 global survey of experts put India as the world's most dangerous country for women.

Solution In 2016, India launched Daughter's Day. It is now celebrated on the last Sunday in September to celebrate daughters, daughters-in-law and granddaughters. The aim is to educate girls and women and improve the way they are treated.

Reaction I was shocked to hear that India is so dangerous for women.

Actions I will treat everyone equally. I can discuss what gender equality means with my family. I will talk to my friends about images in the media that show women as inferior or less intelligent compared to men.

VOCABULARY BOX

1 disadvantaged 2 empower 3 encourage 4 equality 5 exploitation 6 forced 7 gender
8 genital mutilation 9 inferior 10 intelligent 11 launched 12 managerial 13 marriage
14 participate 15 political 16 potential 17 proportion 18 public 19 recognize 20 spheres
21 trafficking 22 value 23 violence

Step4 Research something to do with the topic. Write around 150 words. Use some of the useful expressions, if you like.

Possible Research Topics

Hints

- ☐ Gender equality
- ☐ Women's work at home
- ☐ Women in political, economic, or public positions
- ☐ Domestic violence

In my country

Title

Introduction

Problem

Solution

Reaction

Actions

Reference

Step5 After writing, share your ideas with your friends.

CLEAN WATER AND SANITATION

Ensure access to water and sanitation for all

BY: MARGREET DE HEER

FACT BOX

① More than 785 million people do not have basic safe drinking water services.
② By 2030, 700 million people might have to move due to extreme lack of water.
③ About 30% of the world's population lives without basic sanitation.

Step2 Check your understanding by answering the questions.

Q&A

 Q1: What must we provide everyone with?

 Q2: What do communities need more awareness of?

 FACT BOX Q3: By 2030, how many people will need to move due to extreme lack of water?

 FACT BOX Q4: What percentage of the world's population lives without basic sanitation?

 Q5: Do you think your country has clean water and sanitation?

Step3 Read the sample sentences to get some ideas for writing.

 **Overseas**

Title	Good sanitation

Introduction	We need to ensure access to water and sanitation for all.

Problem	Tonle Sap Lake in Cambodia is the largest freshwater lake in Southeast Asia. Over one million people live around the lake or in floating houses. However, in the floating houses there were no traditional sanitation solutions, so the lake became polluted with sewage. Children especially began to suffer illnesses from polluted drinking and bathing water.

Solution	In 2010, a company called "Wetlands Work!" created a natural sanitation solution named the "HandyPod" using water hyacinths, water plants that are known to cause problems. The pod is put under a floating house's toilet and captures the sewage. The water hyacinths then filter and process it.

Reaction	I was impressed that the company found such a clever solution using natural materials.

Actions	I should be thankful that we have running water and good sanitation. I will conserve water when brushing my teeth and taking baths or showers.

VOCABULARY BOX

1 awareness 2 captures 3 conserve 4 floating houses 5 freshwater 6 hygiene
7 management 8 responsible 9 reuse 10 sanitation 11 sewage 12 water hyacinths
13 well-monitored

Step4 Research something to do with the topic. Write around 150 words. Use some of the useful expressions, if you like.

Possible Research Topics

Hints

- ☐ Good sanitation
- ☐ Using less water
- ☐ Water quality
- ☐ Future water supply

In my country

Title

Introduction

Problem

Solution

Reaction

Actions

Reference

Step5 After writing, share your ideas with your friends.

7 AFFORDABLE AND CLEAN ENERGY

AFFORDABLE AND CLEAN ENERGY

Goal 7

Ensure access to affordable, reliable, sustainable and modern energy

BY: MARGREET DE HEER

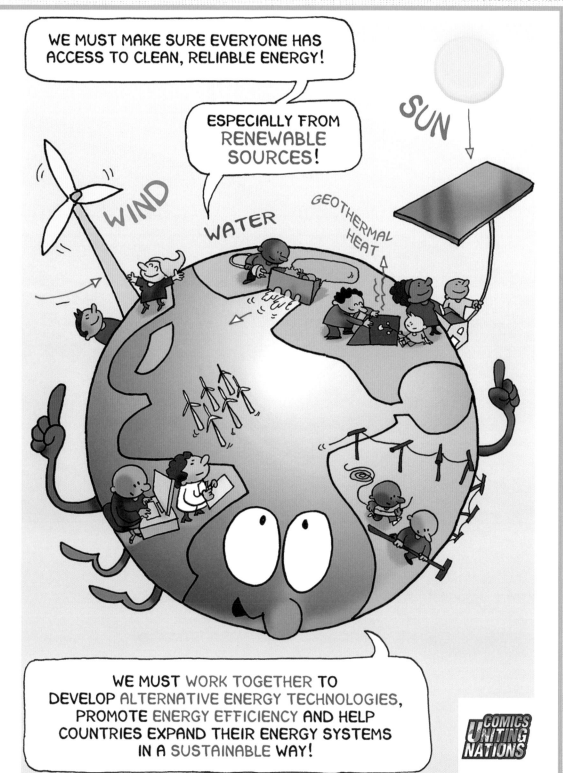

FACT BOX

① 840 million people do not have electricity access.
② 3 billion people lack clean cooking fuels and technology.
③ About 82% of the world's energy use is still from non-renewable sources such as fossil fuels.

Step 2 Check your understanding by answering the questions.

Q&A

👆 **Q1:** Can you name all the renewable energy sources in the picture?

👆 **Q2:** What must we work together to develop?

FACT BOX **Q3:** How many people do not have access to electricity?

FACT BOX **Q4:** How many people lack clean cooking fuels and technology?

💡 **Q5:** What fossil fuels do you use in your country?

Step3 Read the sample sentences to get some ideas for writing.

Sample Sentences **Overseas**

Title Alternative energy technology

Introduction We must ensure access to affordable, reliable, sustainable, and modern energy.

Problem Everyone knows that fossil fuels are not a long-term solution to the world's energy needs. Their stocks are rapidly decreasing and they increase carbon dioxide in the atmosphere, which makes pollution and global warming worse. About 50 years ago, 92 percent of Denmark's energy came from imported oil. In 1973, an oil crisis caused serious problems for the economy and people's daily lives. The government decided to rethink its energy policy completely.

Solution It invested in a variety of alternative energy sources, especially wind. By 2017, Denmark got 43 percent of its energy from wind farms— more than any other country.

Reaction I really respect Denmark's government for trying to think of a long-term solution.

Actions I can find out where the energy I use comes from. I can ride a bike instead of a car. I can conserve energy by not setting air conditioners too cold in summer or too hot in winter.

VOCABULARY BOX

1 affordable 2 alternative 3 atmosphere 4 carbon dioxide 5 develop 6 efficiency
7 electricity 8 energy 9 expand 10 fossil 11 fuels 12 geothermal heat 13 invested
14 pollution 15 reliable 16 renewable 17 sources

Step4 Research something to do with the topic. Write around 150 words. Use some of the useful expressions, if you like.

Hints

Possible Research Topics

- ☐ Alternative energy technology
- ☐ Fossil fuels
- ☐ Using less energy
- ☐ The price of energy (electricity and gas)

In my country

Title

Introduction

Problem

Solution

Reaction

Actions

Reference

Step5 After writing, share your ideas with your friends.

8 DECENT WORK AND ECONOMIC GROWTH

DECENT WORK AND ECONOMIC GROWTH

Goal 8

Promote inclusive and sustainable economic growth, employment and decent work for all

BY: MARGREET DE HEER

"DECENT WORK"...?

WHAT DOES THAT MEAN?

IT MEANS WE HAVE TO MAKE SURE...

1. EVERYONE CAN FREELY CHOOSE A SAFE, FAIRLY PAID, SECURE AND FULFILLING JOB

2. BUSINESSES USE NATURAL RESOURCES WISELY

3. NO ONE IS EXCLUDED FROM WORK OPPORTUNITIES

MEN AND WOMEN   PEOPLE WITH DISABILITIES   YOUNG PEOPLE   MIGRANT WORKERS

4. UNEMPLOYMENT IS REDUCED BY PROVIDING TRAINING

TRAINING

JOB

5. TO END AND PREVENT CHILD LABOR, FORCED LABOR AND MODERN SLAVERY

SCHOOL

6. EVERYONE CAN BENEFIT FROM A GROWING ECONOMY

FUTURE

JOB

COMICS UNITING NATIONS

FACT BOX

① GDP in the poorest countries grew by 4.8% each year between 2010 and 2017. The target is 7%.

② One-fifth(1/5) of young people are not in education, employment, or training (NEETs).

③ About 5% of the world's population is unemployed.

Step 2 Check your understanding by answering the questions.

Q&A

 Q1: What kind of job should everyone be able to choose?

 Q2: Who should not be excluded from work opportunities?

 Q3: What fraction of young people in the world are NEETs?

 Q4: What percentage of the world's population is unemployed?

 Q5: How can you improve your chances of getting decent work?

Step3 Read the sample sentences to get some ideas for writing.

Sample Sentences Overseas

Title Decent work

Introduction We should promote inclusive and sustainable economic growth, employment, and decent work for all.

Problem The International Labour Organization (ILO) estimated that 40 million people were victims of modern slavery in 2016. This means they are forced to work or have limited freedom. Every year, the government of Uzbekistan forces thousands of citizens, including teachers, doctors, and nurses, to leave their daily jobs and harvest cotton. However, the government did not admit that they were doing this.

Solution In 2007, the Anti-Slavery Society began to work with the Cotton Campaign to stop forced labor. As a result, some companies refused to use Uzbek cotton. The Uzbek government finally admitted that forced labor existed and agreed to try to stop it.

Reaction I could not believe that a government forced people to work in the fields like slaves.

Actions I can find out about the brands I buy and refuse to buy brands that use forced or child labor. I will choose a job that helps to achieve the SDGs.

VOCABULARY BOX

1 admit 2 benefit 3 decent 4 disabilities 5 economic growth 6 employment
7 estimated 8 excluded 9 fairly paid 10 fulfilling 11 harvest 12 migrant
13 natural resources 14 reduced 15 secure 16 slavery 17 victims

Step4 Research something to do with the topic. Write around 150 words. Use some of the useful expressions, if you like.

Possible Research Topics

Hints

☐ Decent work

☐ Environmentally friendly brands and businesses

☐ Work opportunities for everyone

☐ Economic growth for everyone

In my country

Title

Introduction

Problem

Solution

Reaction

Actions

Reference

Step5 After writing, share your ideas with your friends.

INDUSTRY, INNOVATION AND INFRASTRUCTURE

Goal 9

Build resilient infrastructure, promote sustainable industrialization and foster innovation

BY: MARGREET DE HEER

FACT BOX

① Many poor countries still have poor basic infrastructure like roads, information and communication technologies, sanitation, power, and water.

② 3.8 billion people (80% of the population of the poorest countries) do not have access to the Internet.

③ Industrialization in the poorest countries is still too slow to meet the 2030 target.

Step2 Check your understanding by answering the questions.

 Q&A

 Q1: What do we need to expand and improve?

 Q2: What should be affordable for everyone?

 FACT BOX **Q3:** What examples of basic infrastructure are given?

 FACT BOX **Q4:** How many people in the world do not have access to the Internet?

 Q5: Do you think the Internet is important? Why?

Step3 Read the sample sentences to get some ideas for writing.

Sample Sentences Overseas

Title Improving infrastructure

Introduction We need to build resilient infrastructure, promote sustainable industrialization, and foster innovation.

Problem It is estimated that around one billion people in the world have no electricity, and 80 percent of them live in rural areas. The group of islands of Vanuatu, near Australia, are small, remote communities. Only four of the 83 islands are big enough to have traditional electricity grids with power stations. The Vanuatu government needed a solution to provide reliable electricity sources for the smaller islands.

Solution They decided to use Power-Blox—an innovative solar-powered battery created by a Swiss company. Power-Blox can be joined together like LEGO® blocks to make portable power grids of different sizes. These are both affordable and environmentally friendly.

Reaction I did not know that there were so many people in the world who have no electricity.

Actions I will keep up to date with the latest technology and innovations. I will give away or recycle old gadgets instead of throwing them away.

VOCABULARY BOX

1 connected 2 credit 3 foster 4 gadgets 5 industrialization 6 industry 7 infrastructure
8 innovation 9 resilient 10 rural

Step4 Research something to do with the topic. Write around 150 words. Use some of the useful expressions, if you like.

Hints

Possible Research Topics

- ☐ Improving infrastructure
- ☐ Useful innovation
- ☐ Recycling
- ☐ Internet access for everyone

In my country

Title

Introduction

Problem

Solution

Reaction

Actions

 **Reference**

Step5 After writing, share your ideas with your friends.

10 REDUCED INEQUALITIES

REDUCED INEQUALITIES
Reduce inequality within and among countries

Goal 10

BY: MARGREET DE HEER

FACT BOX

① The highest gross domestic product (GDP) average per person in the world is more than 100 times greater than the lowest.

② Women living in rural areas are 3 times more likely to die while giving birth than women living in urban centers.

③ 80% of people with disabilities live in the world's developing countries.

Step 2 Check your understanding by answering the questions.

Q&A

 Q1: What must be protected and respected for all people?

 Q2: What does "equal opportunities and rights" mean?

 FACT BOX **Q3:** How many times greater is the highest GDP average per person in the world than the lowest?

 FACT BOX **Q4:** How much more likely are women in rural areas to die while giving birth than those living in urban centers?

 Q5: What inequalities do you think exist in your country?

Step3 Read the sample sentences to get some ideas for writing.

Sample Sentences **Overseas**

Title Equality in all parts of the country

Introduction We must reduce inequality within and among countries.

Problem We cannot achieve the SDGs if some people do not get the opportunities, services, and the benefits of economic growth. In China, two new billionaires are created every week, yet three percent live in poverty. That is a big problem when the population is 1.4 billion. Thirty million of China's poor live in remote areas without running water or electricity.

Solution In 2015, the Chinese government developed an app to support these areas. Villagers upload information about things like health, diet, energy, and education, so the government can provide help quickly. Villagers also use the app to sell crops or raise money for medical supplies and school equipment. It has already helped more than seven million citizens.

Reaction This made me wonder whether there are poorer parts and richer parts in my country.

Actions I will talk to my friends about what inequality means. I will respect people who do things differently or come from different backgrounds to me. I will read more books and watch more movies about different cultures.

VOCABULARY BOX

1 app 2 billionaires 3 border 4 discriminate 5 equipment 6 human rights 7 inequalities
8 laws 9 medical supplies 10 practices 11 representation 12 respected 13 upload 14 urban

Step4 Research something to do with the topic. Write around 150 words. Use some of the useful expressions, if you like. **Hints**

Possible Research Topics

- ☐ Equality in all parts of the country
- ☐ Equality at school and home
- ☐ Protecting people with disabilities
- ☐ Equal opportunities for everyone

In my country

Title

Introduction

Problem

Solution

Reaction

Actions

 **Reference**

Step5 After writing, share your ideas with your friends.

SUSTAINABLE CITIES AND COMMUNITIES

Make cities inclusive, safe, resilient and sustainable

BY: MARGREET DE HEER

FACT BOX

① 60% of the world's population will live in cities by 2030.
② 2 billion people do not have regular waste-collection services.
③ Only half of urban residents have convenient access to transportation.

Step2 Check your understanding by answering the questions.

Q&A

 Q1: How should cities and communities be?

_____
_____
_____

 Q2: What must everyone have access to?

_____
_____
_____

 Q3: By 2030, what percentage of the world's population will live in cities?

_____
_____
_____

 Q4: What fraction of urban residents have convenient access to transportation?

_____
_____
_____

 Q5: How safe is the place you live in?

_____
_____
_____

Step3 Read the sample sentences to get some ideas for writing.

Sample Sentences Overseas

| Title | Air quality |

| Introduction | We need to make cities inclusive, safe, resilient, and sustainable. |

| Problem | Living in cities is convenient, but there are problems as well. Mexico City is in a high-altitude valley which acts like a trap for pollution. In the 1970s and 1980s, its air quality was so bad that breathing it was like smoking several packs of cigarettes every day. The main cause was emissions from cars. |

| Solution | The city became the first in the world to limit car usage. It also expanded public transport and introduced stricter vehicle emissions standards. Air quality improved greatly. |

| Reaction | I wonder if the people who lived in Mexico City during the 1970s and 1980s developed any health problems. |

| Actions | I can use public transport rather than ask my parents to drive me places. I want to find out about air quality in my city. I can look after my own community and pick up trash on the street. I can take an interest in my local community and create an online guide or vlog. I can welcome new residents to my community. |

VOCABULARY BOX

1 adaptable 2 appreciation 3 emissions 4 engage 5 harmful 6 high-altitude
7 improvement 8 monitoring 9 organized 10 residents 11 transportation 12 vehicle
13 vlog 14 waste-collection 15 waste management

Step4 Research something to do with the topic. Write around 150 words. Use some of the useful expressions, if you like.

Possible Research Topics

Hints

- ☐ Air quality
- ☐ Decreasing and managing waste
- ☐ Emissions from cars
- ☐ Keeping cities clean

In my country

Title

Introduction

Problem

Solution

Reaction

Actions

Reference

Step5 After writing, share your ideas with your friends.

RESPONSIBLE CONSUMPTION AND PRODUCTION

Ensure sustainable consumption and production patterns

Goal 12

BY: MARGREET DE HEER

WE MUST MAKE SURE THE PRODUCTION PROCESS FROM MANUFACTURER TO CONSUMER DOES NO HARM TO NATURE NOR HUMANITY AND GENERATES AS LITTLE WASTE AS POSSIBLE!

COMPANIES MUST BE OPEN AND RESPONSIBLE ABOUT THEIR PRACTICES.

WE MUST HAVE INTERNATIONAL AGREEMENTS FOR THE HANDLING OF HARMFUL CHEMICALS.

PROTECTING WATER, AIR & SOIL

WE MUST PREVENT FOOD WASTE!

SALE

SECOND-HAND GOODS

AND KEEP THE PUBLIC INFORMED AND EDUCATED!

COMICS UNITING NATIONS

FACT BOX

① If the population of the earth reaches 9.6 billion by 2050, and we continue using resources the way we do now, we will need 3 planets' worth of resources.

② About one-third(1/3) of the food produced for human consumption each year is lost or wasted.

③ The world's rivers and lakes are polluted much faster than nature can recycle and purify.

Step2 Check your understanding by answering the questions.

Q&A

 Q1: How must companies be?

 Q2: What must manufacturers protect?

 [FACT BOX] **Q3:** What will happen if the population of the earth reaches 9.6 billion by 2050, and we keep using resources in the same way?

[FACT BOX] **Q4:** How much of the world's food is lost or wasted each year?

 Q5: What resources do you think could be used more responsibly in your country?

Read the sample sentences to get some ideas for writing.

Sample Sentences **Overseas**

Title Reducing food waste

Introduction We need to ensure sustainable consumption and production patterns.

Problem Around one billion more people are predicted to be living on the planet by 2030. If we continue wasting resources, in the future there will be shortages. Over seven million tons of food are wasted annually in France. Although the majority of this is wasted by consumers at home, 11 percent is wasted by shops.

Solution In 2016, France became the first country to ban large supermarkets from throwing away or destroying unsold food. Instead, they must donate it to a food bank, or use it for animal feed or fertilizers for farms.

Reaction It scares me a little to think that we will need three planets' worth of resources in the future.

Actions What are some ways I can be a more responsible consumer? I can make sure my family does not buy or serve more food than we need. I can give away clothes, bags, or shoes that someone else could use. I can make sure my family recycles everything we can.

VOCABULARY BOX

1 agreements 2 animal feed 3 chemicals 4 consumer 5 consumption 6 educated
7 fertilizers 8 generates 9 goods 10 handling 11 harm 12 humanity 13 informed
14 manufacturer 15 planets 16 predicted 17 production 18 purify 19 resources
20 shortages 21 soil

Step4 Research something to do with the topic. Write around 150 words. Use some of the useful expressions, if you like.

Hints
- ☐ Reducing food waste
- ☐ 9.6 billion people on Earth by 2050
- ☐ A responsible consumer
- ☐ Protecting the water, air, and soil

In my country

Title

Introduction

Problem

Solution

Reaction

Actions

Reference

Step5 After writing, share your ideas with your friends.

13 CLIMATE ACTION

CLIMATE ACTION

Take urgent action to combat climate change and its impacts

Goal 13

BY: MARGREET DE HEER

Step1 Find out about the goal by reading the comic and the fact box.

FACT BOX

① 97% of climate scientists agree that global warming over the past century is due to human activities.
② Sea levels have risen by almost 19 cm in the past 100 years.
③ The planet has warmed about 1°C since the end of the 19th century.

Step2 Check your understanding by answering the questions.

Q&A

Q1: What has influenced climate change in the last 200 years?

Q2: What must we be prepared to do?

FACT BOX **Q3:** How many centimeters have sea levels risen in the past 100 years?

FACT BOX **Q4:** How many degrees has the world's temperature gone up since the end of the 19th century?

Q5: What do you think has happened and will happen as a result of climate change?

Step3 Read the sample sentences to get some ideas for writing.

Sample Sentences **Overseas**

Title Smart cities

Introduction We must take urgent action to combat climate change and its impacts.

Problem Cities are a major cause of climate change. They consume more than two-thirds of the world's energy and generate more than 70 percent of global CO_2 emissions. If we want to stop climate change, we must find ways to make cities more environmentally friendly.

Solution In 2014, Valencia became the first "smart city" in Spain by creating an online system for 45 different city services. This helps the council to run the city more efficiently and people who live there to reduce their environmental impact. Smart lighting and smart water management have reduced consumption by up to 35 percent. Traffic cameras, intelligent traffic lights, and realtime parking updates are reducing traffic jams.

Reaction Climate change really concerns me. I think science and technology could help us save the planet.

Actions I will educate myself about climate change. I will encourage my family to drive less, especially during the busiest times. I can unplug my computer and other electronics when not in use.

VOCABULARY BOX

1 added 2 behavior 3 climate 4 combat 5 council 6 decades 7 degrees 8 droughts
9 extreme weather 10 impacts 11 influence 12 measures 13 mitigate 14 nations 15 policies
16 resilience 17 reverse 18 sea levels 19 sturdy 20 temperature 21 thinning ozone layer
22 traffic 23 unplug 24 urgent

Step4 Research something to do with the topic. Write around 150 words. Use some of the useful expressions, if you like.

Hints

Possible Research Topics

☐ Smart cities
☐ Extreme weather
☐ Using less electricity
☐ Building resilient, sustainable cities

In my country

Title

Introduction

Problem

Solution

Reaction

Actions

 **Reference**

Step5 After writing, share your ideas with your friends.

LIFE BELOW WATER

Conserve and sustainably use the oceans, seas and marine resources

Goal 14

BY: MARGREET DE HEER

MOST OF THE PLANET'S SURFACE IS WATER! HERE'S WHAT WE MUST DO TO PROTECT THE OCEANS:

1. REDUCE AND PREVENT POLLUTION

2. PROTECT ECOSYSTEMS

3. END OVERFISHING AND ILLEGAL FISHING

4. HELP FISHING COMMUNITIES TO DEVELOP SUSTAINABLE FISHING PRACTICES

5. SCIENTIFIC COOPERATION
- TO INCREASE KNOWLEDGE
- TO IMPROVE TECHNOLOGIES
- TO MINIMIZE OCEAN ACIDIFICATION

6. MAKE AND MAINTAIN INTERNATIONAL LAWS

AGREEMENTS

COMICS UNITING NATIONS

FACT BOX

① About 70% of the earth's surface is covered with oceans and seas. We rely on them for food, energy, and water.

② Over 3 billion people rely on sea and coastal biodiversity.

③ 40% of the world's oceans suffer from overfishing, poor fishing practices, and poor waste management.

Step2 Check your understanding by answering the questions.

Q&A

 Q1: What covers most of the earth's surface?

 Q2: What can we do to protect the oceans?

 Q3: What do we rely on oceans and seas for?

 Q4: What do 40 percent of the world's oceans suffer from?

 Q5: Can you think of any other reasons that the oceans and seas are important?

Step3 Read the sample sentences to get some ideas for writing.

Sample Sentences **Overseas**

Title Reducing plastics in the oceans

Introduction We need to conserve and sustainably use the oceans, seas, and marine resources.

Problem Pollution on beaches and in the oceans causes harm to marine life and humans. One of the biggest problems is plastic, as it does not break down like natural materials. Some experts believe that in 30 years there will be more plastic in the oceans than fish. After China, Indonesia is the world's second largest contributor to marine plastic pollution.

Solution Tiza Mafira is an Indonesian lawyer and activist. In 2015, her organization launched a petition asking shops to stop giving out plastic bags for free. The following year, the government introduced a plastic bag charge. After six months, there was a 55 percent reduction in the use of plastic bags.

Reaction I was amazed when I heard that there will be more plastic in the oceans than fish.

Actions I can refuse unnecessary plastics. I will buy a reusable water bottle. I can say no to plastic straws when ordering a drink. I can organize a beach-cleaning trip with my friends.

VOCABULARY BOX

1 acidification 2 activist 3 biodiversity 4 charge 5 coastal 6 contributor 7 cooperation
8 ecosystems 9 knowledge 10 maintain 11 marine 12 organize 13 overfishing
14 petition

Step4 Research something to do with the topic. Write around 150 words. Use some of the useful expressions, if you like.

Hints

Possible Research Topics

- ☐ Reducing plastics in the oceans
- ☐ Reducing pollution
- ☐ Ending overfishing and illegal fishing
- ☐ Cleaning beaches and rivers

In my country

Title

Introduction

Problem

Solution

Reaction

Actions

Reference

Step5 After writing, share your ideas with your friends.

LIFE ON LAND

Sustainably manage forests, combat desertification, halt and reverse land degradation, halt biodiversity loss

BY: MARGREET DE HEER

Step 1 Find out about the goal by reading the comic and the fact box.

FACT BOX

① 2.6 billion people depend on agriculture. 52% of the land used for agriculture is badly affected by soil degradation.

② Between 2010 and 2015, the world lost 3.3 million hectares of forest. Forests are home to more than 80% of all species of land animals, plants, and insects.

③ There are around 8,300 well-known animal types. 8% of these are now extinct, and 22% are at risk of extinction.

Step 2 Check your understanding by answering the questions.

Q&A

 Q1: What are humans a part of?

 Q2: What can we do to conserve and protect plant and animal life on land?

 Q3: How many people depend directly on agriculture?

 Q4: What percentage of known animal breeds are at risk of extinction?

 Q5: Do you think forests are important? Why?

Step3 Read the sample sentences to get some ideas for writing.

Sample Sentences **Overseas**

Title Endangered species

Introduction We must sustainably manage forests, combat desertification, halt and reverse land degradation, and halt biodiversity loss.

Problem In 2002, the blue iguana, a lizard which was only found on the Cayman Islands, was critically endangered with only 10-25 remaining in the wild. Human-introduced threats, such as cars and non-native animals, such as dogs and cats, had damaged the island's ecosystem and wiped out the iguanas.

Solution A group of volunteers started the Blue Iguana Recovery Program. Starting with about 10 captive iguanas, they rebuilt the population. In 2012, the lizards were taken off the critically endangered list. By 2018, there were more than 1,000 iguanas in nature reserves on Grand Cayman and their numbers are still increasing.

Reaction It makes me sad to think that humans are causing so many animals to become endangered or extinct.

Actions I will support companies that take conservation of nature seriously. I will respect all plant and animal life.

VOCABULARY BOX

1 breeds 2 captive 3 critically 4 deforestation 5 degradation 6 desertification
7 endangered species 8 extinct 9 halt 10 human-introduced 11 preserve 12 threats

Step4 Research something to do with the topic. Write around 150 words. Use some of the useful expressions, if you like.

Possible Research Topics

Hints

☐ Endangered species
☐ Planting more trees
☐ Protecting forests
☐ Sustainable farming

In my country

Title

Introduction

Problem

Solution

Reaction

Actions

Reference

Step5 After writing, share your ideas with your friends.

16 PEACE, JUSTICE AND STRONG INSTITUTIONS

PEACE, JUSTICE AND STRONG INSTITUTIONS

Promote just, peaceful and inclusive societies

Goal 16

BY: MARGREET DE HEER

TOO MANY PEOPLE EXPERIENCE WAR AND VIOLENCE! HERE'S WHAT WE MUST DO ABOUT IT:

1. END ALL FORMS OF VIOLENCE

2. ESPECIALLY VIOLENCE AGAINST CHILDREN

3. BIRTH REGISTRATION AND LEGAL IDENTITIES FOR ALL

IDENTITY

4. EQUAL ACCESS TO JUSTICE AND LEGAL INFORMATION FOR ALL

LAW

5. COMBAT CRIME AND CORRUPTION

6. STRENGTHEN INSTITUTIONS SO PEOPLE CAN TRUST THEM

COMICS UNITING NATIONS

Step 1 Find out about the goal by reading the comic and the fact box.

FACT BOX

① 50% of the world's children experience violence every year. Every 5 minutes, somewhere in the world, a child is killed by violence.

② 1 in 3 students has been bullied by their peers at school in the last month. At least 1 in 10 children has experienced cyberbullying.

③ 81% of murder victims are men, but 64% of murder victims in family or partner-related murders are women.

Step 2 Check your understanding by answering the questions.

Q&A

**Q1:** What must we end?

**Q2:** What must we combat?

FACT BOX **Q3:** What percentage of the world's children experience violence every year?

FACT BOX **Q4:** What proportion of children have experienced cyberbullying?

Q5: What institutions help to provide you with peace and justice?

Step3 Read the sample sentences to get some ideas for writing.

Sample Sentences **Overseas**

Title Reducing violence

Introduction We should promote just, peaceful, and inclusive societies.

Problem For over 50 years, the Colombian government has been fighting a war with guerillas. This has led to more than 220,000 people being killed and more than 5.7 million people being forced to move. The guerillas used crime to finance their war, which was bad for Colombian society.

Solution Jose Miguel Sokoloff, a Colombian advertising executive, realized that many guerillas wanted to stop fighting, but felt trapped. At Christmas 2010, his agency placed nine decorated trees in the guerilla-controlled jungles with a sign saying "If Christmas can come to the jungle, you can come home." Thanks to this and other strategies, so many guerillas have now quit fighting that the leaders were forced to talk with the government.

Reaction I think this man is a genius for finding a peaceful solution to violence.

Actions I can visit places like Hiroshima and Ground Zero in New York to learn about world peace. I will take an interest in politics and talk to my friends about it.

VOCABULARY BOX

1 advertising executive 2 corruption 3 crime 4 cyberbullying 5 finance 6 identities
7 institutions 8 just 9 justice 10 legal 11 murder victims 12 partner-related 13 peers
14 registration 15 strategies

Step4 Research something to do with the topic. Write around 150 words. Use some of the useful expressions, if you like.

Hints

Possible Research Topics

☐ Reducing violence
☐ A peaceful and safe society
☐ Peace memorials and museums
☐ Young people voting

In my country

Title

Introduction

Problem

Solution

Reaction

Actions

Reference

Step5 After writing, share your ideas with your friends.

PARTNERSHIPS FOR THE GOALS

Revitalize the global partnership for sustainable development

Goal 17

BY: MARGREET DE HEER

WE MUST MAKE SURE WE MEET THESE GOALS BY 2030!

THEY MUST BE INCLUDED IN NATIONAL PLANS.

ALL COUNTRIES MUST WORK TOGETHER TO IMPLEMENT THE GOALS.

POLICIES AND LAWS BASED ON 17 GOALS

GETTING INVOLVED IN COMMUNITY WORK AND WITH AID ORGANIZATIONS IS A GREAT WAY TO START!

GOVERNMENTS MUST WORK TOGETHER WITH CONCERNED PEOPLE OF ALL AGES IN ORDER TO MAKE PROGRESS ON THE GOALS.

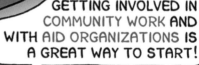

COMICS UNITING NATIONS

FACT BOX

① The United Nations Conference on Trade and Development (UNCTAD) says achieving the SDGs will need $5 trillion to $7 trillion of investment each year.

② Official Development Assistance (ODA) to the poorest countries, which includes economic and technological support, has fallen by 3% since 2017. Assistance to Africa has fallen by 4%.

③ In 2016, only 6 countries met the international target to keep ODA at or above of 0.7% of gross national income.

Step2 Check your understanding by answering the questions.

Q&A

 Q1: By what year must we make sure we meet the goals?

 Q2: Who should work together?

 Q3: What does ODA stand for?

 Q4: How many countries met the ODA target in 2016?

 Q5: What do you think are the most important SDGs in your community or country?

Step3 Read the sample sentences to get some ideas for writing.

Sample Sentences **Overseas**

Title Community work

Introduction We need to revitalize the global partnership for sustainable development.

Problem Over 1.5 million refugees from the war in Syria have fled to Lebanon. The country has a higher percentage of refugees than any other place in the world.

Solution Various United Nations (UN) organizations, the government, and local groups are working together. Local people ensure the refugees are cared for. Local businesses have trained women to provide food to the refugees and neighborhood groups help coordinate everything. A difficult situation has become an opportunity to work together.

Reaction I was amazed to find out how many refugees there are in Lebanon. I wonder if people in my country would work together so well.

Actions I will think globally and act locally. I will be open-minded and generous, and share my ideas and skills. I can join or create a group that wants to achieve the SDGs. I will stay informed, read the news, and think about which SDGs are related to what I am reading.

VOCABULARY BOX

1 aid organizations 2 concerned 3 coordinate 4 development 5 gross national income
6 implement 7 Official Development Assistance (ODA) 8 partnerships 9 refugees
10 revitalize 11 trade 12 trillion

Step4 Research something to do with the topic. Write around 150 words. Use some of the useful expressions, if you like.

Hints

Possible Research Topics

- ☐ Community work
- ☐ ODA from my country
- ☐ Promoting the SDGs
- ☐ Think globally and act locally

In my country

Title

....

Introduction

....

Problem

....

....

....

....

Solution

....

....

....

....

Reaction

....

Actions

....

....

....

 **Reference**

Step5 After writing, share your ideas with your friends.

Question and Answer Ideas

1. NO POVERTY
1 Q: What fraction of the world's population lives in poverty?
A: About half of the world's population lives in poverty.
2 Q: What is "social protection"?
A: It is access to health care and protection against unemployment.
3 Q: What does "extreme poverty" mean?
A: It means living on less than $1.90 per day.
4 Q: What percentage of the world's population has no social protection?
A: About 55 percent of the world's population has no social protection.
5 Q: Do you think your country has a problem with poverty?
A: Yes, I think we have a problem because the number of homeless people seems to be increasing.

2. ZERO HUNGER
1 Q: What does eating only one sort of food cause?
A: It causes all kinds of weaknesses.
2 Q: How can we end malnutrition?
A: We can end malnutrition by improving education and social programs for mothers, children, and the elderly.
3 Q: What is one of the leading causes of death in the world?
A: Hunger is.
4 Q: How many people do not have enough food?
A: More than 820 million people worldwide do not have enough food.
5 Q: Do you think your country has a problem with too much food or too little food?
A: I think we have too much food. / I think we have too little food.

3. GOOD HEALTH AND WELL-BEING
1 Q: What does good health and well-being mean?
A: It means things like living through early childhood.
2 Q: What kind of health care can we provide for all?
A: We can provide access to essential healthcare services, medicines, and vaccination for all.
3 Q: What percentage of women in developing regions receive the health care they need?
A: Only half of women in developing regions receive the health care they need.
4 Q: What is one of the world's largest environmental health risks?
A: Air pollution is. It kills more than seven million people each year.
5 Q: What diseases have you been vaccinated against?
A: I have been vaccinated against influenza and measles.

4. QUALITY EDUCATION
1 Q: When is the best time to start education?
A: The best time is from an early age.
2 Q: What kind of environment is best?
A: A safe, positive, and rights-respecting environment is best.
3 Q: How many adults worldwide cannot read and write?
A: More than 750 million adults still cannot read and write.
4 Q: How many children around the world are not in school?
A: About 57 million elementary age children remain out of school.
5 Q: Do you think you are getting a quality education? Why?
A: I think so because our teachers are well-trained and motivated.

5. GENDER EQUALITY

1 Q: What examples of violence against women and girls are given?
A: The examples given are trafficking, sexual exploitation, forced marriage, and female genital mutilation.

2 Q: What can we encourage women and girls to do?
A: We can encourage them to participate in all political, economic, and public spheres.

3 Q: How many women and girls were married before the age of 18?
A: Almost 750 million women and girls were.

4 Q: What proportion of women and girls have experienced violence by a partner?
A: One in five women and girls has.

5 Q: Do you think the genders are equal in your country?
A: Yes, because all boys and girls can go to school.

6. CLEAN WATER AND SANITATION

1 Q: What must we provide everyone with?
A: We must provide everyone with things such as hygiene education and clean, safe water.

2 Q: What do communities need more awareness of?
A: We need more awareness about improving water management.

3 Q: By 2030, how many people will need to move due to extreme lack of water?
A: More than 700 million people will.

4 Q: What percentage of the world's population lives without basic sanitation?
A: About 30 percent lives without basic sanitation.

5 Q: Do you think your country has clean water and sanitation?
A: Yes, because I can drink water from any tap and we have toilets in our houses.

7. AFFORDABLE AND CLEAN ENERGY

1 Q: Can you name all the renewable energy sources in the picture?
A: They are wind, water, geothermal heat, and sun/solar.

2 Q: What must we work together to develop?
A: We must work together to develop alternative energy technologies, promote energy efficiency, and help countries expand energy systems sustainably.

3 Q: How many people do not have access to electricity?
A: More than 840 million people do not.

4 Q: How many people lack clean cooking fuels and technology?
A: About three billion people do.

5 Q: What fossil fuels do you use in your country?
A: We use gas, coal, and oil.

8. DECENT WORK AND ECONOMIC GROWTH

1 Q: What kind of job should everyone be able to choose?
A: Everyone should be able to choose a safe, fairly paid, secure, and fulfilling job.

2 Q: Who should not be excluded from work opportunities?
A: Men and women, people with disabilities, young people, and migrant workers.

3 Q: What fraction of young people in the world are NEETs?
A: One-fifth of young people are NEETs (not in education, employment, or training).

4 Q: What percentage of the world's population is unemployed?
A: About five percent of the world's population is.

5 Q: How can you improve your chances of getting decent work?
A: I think I should try hard in classes and go to university.

9. INDUSTRY, INNOVATION AND INFRASTRUCTURE

1 Q: What do we need to expand and improve?
A: We need to expand and improve infrastructure.
2 Q: What should be affordable for everyone?
A: Internet access should be.
3 Q: What examples of basic infrastructure are given?
A: Roads, information and communication technologies, sanitation, power, and water.
4 Q: How many people in the world do not have access to the Internet?
A: Around 3.8 billion people (80 percent of the population of the poorest countries) do not have access to the Internet.
5 Q: Do you think the Internet is important? Why?
A: Of course! The Internet is important for communicating, learning about the world, buying and selling things, and entertainment.

10. REDUCED INEQUALITIES

1 Q: What must be protected and respected for all people?
A: Human rights must be protected and respected for all people.
2 Q: What does "equal opportunities and rights" mean?
A: It means laws and practices do not discriminate against anybody.
3 Q: How many times greater is the highest GDP average per person in the world than the lowest?
A: The highest GDP average per person is more than 100 times the lowest.
4 Q: How much more likely are women in rural areas to die while giving birth than those living in urban centers?
A: Women in rural areas are three times more likely to die than women who live in urban centers.
5 Q: What inequalities do you think exist in your country?
A: I think inequalities exist in salaries and educational opportunities.

11. SUSTAINABLE CITIES AND COMMUNITIES

1 Q: How should cities and communities be?
A: Cities and communities should be inclusive, safe, resilient, and sustainable.
2 Q: What must everyone have access to?
A: Everyone must have access to quality, safe housing, and basic services.
3 Q: By 2030, what percentage of the world's population will live in cities?
A: About 60 percent of the world's population will.
4 Q: What fraction of urban residents have convenient access to transportation?
A: Only half of urban residents do.
5 Q: How safe is the place you live in?
A: I think the place I live in is safe because we have police and ambulances to protect us.

12. RESPONSIBLE CONSUMPTION AND PRODUCTION

1 Q: How must companies be?
A: They must be open and responsible about their practices.
2 Q: What must manufacturers protect?
A: They must protect water, air, and soil.
3 Q: What will happen if the population of the earth reaches 9.6 billion by 2050, and we keep using resources in the same way?
A: Three planets worth of resources will be needed.
4 Q: How much of the world's food is lost or wasted each year?
A: About one-third of the food produced for human consumption is lost or wasted.
5 Q: What resources do you think could be used more responsibly in your country?
A: I think we use too much plastic and paper in packaging.

13. CLIMATE ACTION

1 Q: What has influenced climate change in the last 200 years?

A: Human behavior has.

2 Q: What must we be prepared to do?

A: We must be prepared to manage extreme weather and natural disasters.

3 Q: How many centimeters have sea levels risen in the past 100 years?

A: They have risen by almost 19 cm.

4 Q: How many degrees has the world's temperature gone up since the end of the 19th century?

A: The planet has warmed by about 1°C.

5 Q: What do you think has happened and will happen as a result of climate change?

A: I think we will have hotter summers and stronger typhoons.

14. LIFE BELOW WATER

1 Q: What covers most of the earth's surface?

A: Water docs. / Oceans and seas do.

2 Q: What can we do to protect the oceans?

A: We can protect them by doing things like preventing pollution and ending overfishing.

3 Q: What do we rely on oceans and seas for?

A: We rely on them for food, energy, and water.

4 Q: What do 40 percent of the world's oceans suffer from?

A: They suffer from overfishing, poor fishing practices, and poor waste management.

5 Q: Can you think of any other reasons that the oceans and seas are important?

A: We use them for transport and water sports.

15. LIFE ON LAND

1 Q: What are humans a part of?

A: We are a part of the global ecosystem.

2 Q: What can we do to conserve and protect plant and animal life on land?

A: We can do things like plant more trees and protect biodiversity.

3 Q: How many people depend directly on agriculture?

A: Over 2.6 billion people do.

4 Q: What percentage of known animal breeds are at risk of extinction?

A: Around 22 percent are at risk of extinction.

5 Q: Do you think forests are important? Why?

A: Absolutely! One reason they are important is because they produce oxygen.

16. PEACE, JUSTICE AND STRONG INSTITUTIONS

1 Q: What must we end?

A: We need to end all forms of violence (especially against children).

2 Q: What must we combat?

A: We must combat crime and corruption.

3 Q: What percentage of the world's children experience violence every year?

A: About 50 percent of the world's children do.

4 Q: What proportion of children have experienced cyberbullying?

A: At least one in ten children has.

5 Q: What institutions help to provide you with peace and justice?

A: We have many, for example the army, the police, and the legal system.

17. PARTNERSHIPS FOR THE GOALS

1 Q: By what year must we make sure we meet the goals?

A: By 2030.

2 Q: Who should work together?

A: All countries and governments must work together.

3 Q: What does ODA stand for?

A: It stands for Official Development Assistance.

4 Q: How many countries met the ODA target in 2016?

A: Only six countries met the international target.

5 Q: What do you think are the most important SDGs in your community or country?

A: I think responsible consumption because we throw lots of things away that could still be used.

Series 1:TAGAKI ⑩~㊿

Teach Yourself

- Use sample sentences to write good English
- Think and write, then share your ideas
- Develop your interest with 30 x 5 textbooks=150 global topics
- Learn to write with structure: catchy sentences, facts, opinions, and punch lines
- Be independent learners. Evaluate yourself

TAGAKI ⑩ — I can do it! Write and check it by yourself
Learn to write three short sentences about 30 daily topics

TAGAKI ⑳ — Choose your position: agree or disagree
Learn to clearly express your feelings

TAGAKI ㉚ — Pretend to be a third person and write
Learn to write with structure: catchy sentences, facts, opinions, and punch lines

TAGAKI ㊵ — Write two original sentences
Learn to write about global topics

TAGAKI ㊿ — Research a topic for additional facts and write about them
State your opinion and make your own punch lines

TAGAKI Advanced 3 SDGs: Problems and Solutions

First Published 2020
Seventh Published 2023
Writers: Damien Pratt, Yoko Matsuka
Contributors: Miyuki Kasuya, Rieko Kondo
English Proofreader: Glenn McDougall
Production: EDIT Co., Ltd.
Illustrator: Margreet de Heer
Designer: Taira Nakayama
DTP Designer: Taira Design
Photos: amanaimages, imagenavi, istock, PIXTA, Shutterstock, 123RF
Record Producer: JAILHOUSE MUSIC Inc.
Narrators: Carolyn Miller, Howard Colefield, Peter von Gomm, Rumiko Varnes
Printer: Shinano Co., Ltd.
Special thanks to Chisato Mattox, Hiroko Sadano, Hiromi Sasaki, Kazuko Okazaki, Mie Nonaka, Mika Suzuki, Yuri Akamatsu, Aiko Mochizawa, Akiko McDougall, Harumi Onimaru, Kenzo Yoneda, Makoto Kobayashi, Miho Aoyama Tamagawa University UNESCO Club

Download the audio files from the QR code or web page.
https://www.mpi-j.co.jp/contents/shop/mpi/contents/digital/tagaki_advanced_03.html

Publisher: mpi Matsuka Phonics inc.
No.2 Koda Bldg 2F 2-16-2 Yoyogi,
Shibuya-ku, Tokyo 151-0053 Japan
fax:03-5302-1652
URL: https://www.mpi-j.co.jp/
ISBN 978-4-89643-778-2
Printed in Japan